Milo's
Christmas
Adventures

A Holiday Academic
Coloring Workbook

ISBN: (paperback) 978-1-7368896-3-3

Milo's
Christmas
Adventures

"Let the magic of the season fill your heart."
April Stults

Milo woke Lex up
early one morning with
a special surprise but
Lex was very confused.

There was an
evergreen
inside their
home.

As Milo explained the history of Christmas, Lex got himself tangled in the twinkle lights. They decorated the Christmas tree with ornaments and tinsel.

With the tree complete, Milo started a nice warm fire.

Lex wasn't too sure about the fireplace and stayed back as...

...Milo showed him their special stockings.

Making it a point to
turn off the TV, Milo
taught Lex how to
wrap a gift. It is,
after all, the season
of giving.

Wrapping presents is quite the challenge for a puppy.

Exhausted by so much teaching,
Milo showed Lex his snow globe.

In an instant, Lex ran to the window and started barking. It was snowing outside, just like inside Milo's snow globe!

Oh, what a connection!

Vocabulary

evergreen - *noun.* having leaves that remain green all year long. Most pine trees are evergreens.

history - *noun.* past events.

twinkle - *noun.* a sparkle or flicker of light.

tangle - *verb.* to become or cause something to become twisted together.

tinsel - *noun.* thin strip of shiny metal or paper that are used as decoration.

exhausted - *verb.* to tire out or wear out completely.

snow globe - *noun.* decorative object or toy containing fluid with suspended white flakes that look like snow when shaken.

connection- *noun.* something that joins two or more things or ideas.

Discussion -

What is your favorite part of getting ready for Christmas? and Why?

Snow

tiny little flakes
fall gracefully
from a cloud

lay gently
and wait patiently
for ones imagination

with gloved hands
and a builder's eye
soon, a snowman
will arise.

-April Stults

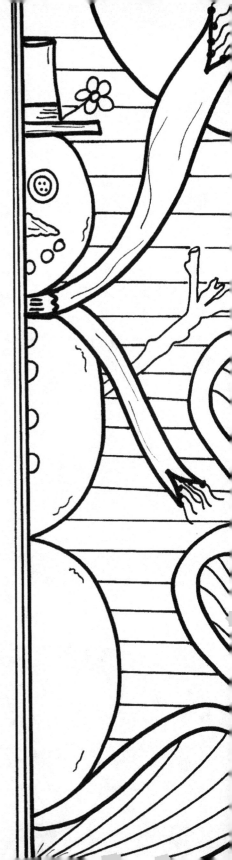

```
                        T
                    I   Z   D
                F   E   H   E   S
            S   T   D   L   C   T   M
        C   I   N   S   E   O   O   T   H
            E   T   D   R   C
        P   M   H   K   A   K   Z
        N   C   A   G   V   T   I   O   E
    V   T   M   N   I   R   I   N   S   B   I
T   I   Q   V   R   L   T   O   G   G   O   B   N
O   C   T   S   E   O   L   H   N   C   E   L   I   Y   F
    F   Q   Q   R   V   S   A   F   G
        A   Y   D   G   M   W   C   P   V   W   V
    O   P   R   E   S   E   N   T   S   X   O   P   B
R   I   L   T   T   Q   K   E   A   A   E   N   T   J   N
A   F   I   R   E   P   L   A   C   E   O   L   S   I   V   N   I
S   T   R   E   E   A   D   X   O   L   I   M   U   L   E   P   P   P   K
                    Y
                    S
                    X
```

WORD LIST:

DECORATIONS	ORNAMENT
FIREPLACE	PRESENTS
LEX	SNOWGLOBE
LIGHTS	STOCKING
MILO	TREE

Stockings

What's inside,
a sweet surprise?
A tiny toy?
A glimmering jewel?
A bite-sized delight?

They hang in waiting
for days on end
expecting a fill
from the giver of gifts,

And on that morning
when shiny wrapped
presents lay under the tree,
remember your stocking
is waiting for you.

April Stults

White puffy snowflakes fell silently from the sky. Milo sat by and watched Lex try to catch them in his mouth.

Lex had never seen snow before
and was surprised by how cold
and wet it was.

Milo put mittens on his puppy's paws and brought out the snowman items box.

A hat for his head, and carrot for his nose...

...but Lex couldn't help wonder if they'd also put him in a globe.

As their day turned to night, Lex
ran into a new friend. Milo had
already met the fine fellow,

...but Lex wondered...

"What's a reindeer do?"

As Milo
explained, Lex
imagined...

...the super long trip those reindeer must make.

"Merry Christmas, Santa!"

At the end of the night, with his puppy finally resting, mischievous Milo waited. As quiet as a mouse, behind the sofa he sat, he caught a glimpse of the giver of gifts.

"Ho, ho, ho,
Merry Christmas Milo
and sweet
little Lex!"

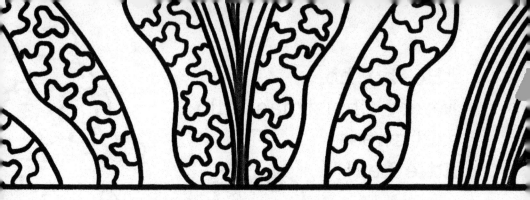

Draw/Doodle a picture of something you are asking for this holiday season.

Twinkle Lights

A gleam catches my eye
and sparks memories
of days filled with laughter
and wonder.

Ornaments and tinsel
decorate an evergreen
like armor in the night
as if waiting for
something magical to happen,

And it did, didn't it?
We'd gone to sleep,
whispered wishes,
and prayers on that night
and upon the sunrise
a gift, the present,
lay waiting
under twinkle lights.

April Stults

Stars

Up high
they shine
for all to see

look up,
they say,
a marvel
at its grandeur

but I look
at you
and marvel
at your sparkle
for you are my star,
my dear.

April Stults

written for her children

M S F K Q J S X
D U S F A O W E C A Z J
T L V V R T F B D W L T J K
P P R S T K Y S C G Y V A C Y J
U D J O X O N X E G N Q N N G Q S Z
R G R W U R O C K R E C H F Z E B A
V R Q R E Z S R R A K Z J Z Y G E Q F S
A C K E H S A T S L O G N I S Q P Q V J
L Q E G T R N H T F K U S U G N G V M D
B S Y J D O T P F F Z B I O L Q J T F H
Y G V R N O A O I B H V V D M Y Q S I P
K J T T U D G L G W W Z J N V H T L U H
W Q U F O T R E C U M B O H T N F T O X
D M O E R U E L A S L E D T B E P Y T L
C G E A O U W Q V L N A M W O N S F
B W U N D Y X V T Z A P Q W W K M H
C Y W G E R E M K V S I N E J T
B E E R C R E E D N I E R W
A P A I A P H H J B X O
Z S D N E I R F

WORD LIST:

AROUND THE WORLD
FLAKE
FRIENDS
GIFTS
NORTH POLE

OUTDOORS
REINDEER
SANTA
SLED
SNOWMAN

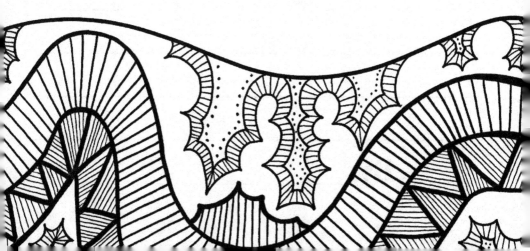

Christmas List

_____

_____

_____

_____

_____

_____

_____

_____

_____

_____

_____

_____

By: _____

Presents

What is a gift
if not something
meant to bring
happiness.

Is that found in a box
or in the heart?

Does not the giver
find happiness
in giving,
as much as
the receiver
finds
happiness
in receiving?

April Stults

YOUR DOODLES

Educator Approved for ages 7-12

Thank you for choosing
Milo the Doodle Cat.
Collect them all!

Book 1   Book 2   Book 3

For more news on Milo,
book signings, events, etc. visit:
www.aprilstultsbooks.com

Thank you for the: Likes, Saves, Shares,
Reviews, Story Posts, and all the Love!

CPSIA information can be obtained
at www.ICGtesting.com
Printed in the USA
LVHW081802171121
703478LV00018B/145

9 781736 889633